THE COMPLETE PIANO PLAYER
ROCK 'N' ROLL

Arranged by Kenneth Baker

KU-178-607

This publication is not authorised for sale in
the United States of America and/or Canada.

Wise Publications
London/New York/Paris/Sydney/Copenhagen/Madrid

Exclusive Distributors:
Music Sales Limited
8/9 Frith Street,
London W1V 5TZ,
England.
Music Sales Pty Limited
120 Rothschild Avenue,
Rosebery, NSW 2018,
Australia.

This book © Copyright 1996 by Wise Publications
Order No. AM92589
ISBN 0-7119-4666-3

Unauthorised reproduction of any part of this publication by any
means including photocopying is an infringement of copyright.

Compiled by Peter Evans
Music arranged by Kenneth Baker
Music processed by MSS Studios

Book design by Pearce Marchbank, Studio Twenty, London
Quarked by Ben May

Cover photograph courtesy of:
REX Features

Your Guarantee of Quality
As publishers, we strive to produce every book to the
highest commercial standards.
The music has been freshly engraved and the book has been
carefully designed to minimise awkward page turns and to
make playing from it a real pleasure.
Particular care has been given to specifying acid-free,
neutral-sized paper made from pulps which have not been elemental chlorine bleached.
This pulp is from farmed sustainable forests and was produced with
special regard for the environment.
Throughout, the printing and binding have been planned to ensure a sturdy,
attractive publication which should give years of enjoyment.
If your copy fails to meet our high standards, please
inform us and we will gladly replace it.

Music Sales' complete catalogue describes thousands of titles and is
available in full colour sections by subject, direct from Music Sales Limited.
Please state your areas of interest and send a cheque/postal order for £1.50 for postage to:
Music Sales Limited, Newmarket Road, Bury St. Edmunds, Suffolk IP33 3YB.

Printed in the United Kingdom by
Printwise (Haverhill) Limited, Haverhill, Suffolk.

(LET ME BE YOUR) TEDDY BEAR

Words & Music by Kal Mann & Bernie Lowe

© Copyright 1957 Gladys Music, USA.
Carlin Music Corporation, Iron Bridge House, 3 Bridge Approach, London NW1
for the territory of UK, Eire & the British Dominions, Colonies, Overseas Territories
and Dependencies (excluding Canada, Australia & New Zealand).
All Rights Reserved. International Copyright Secured.

5

TUTTI FRUTTI

Words & Music by Richard Penniman, D La Bostrie & Joe Lubin

© Copyright 1955 Venice Music Incorporated, USA.
ATV Music for the UK, Eire, British Commonwealth (excluding Canada & Australasia) & the Continent of Europe.
All Rights Reserved. International Copyright Secured.

3. I gotta go, can't stop,
   Down to the candy shop.
   I gotta go, can't stop,
   And get me an ice cream pop.
   Don't want vanilla or strawberry too,
   Want the same kind of flavour when I'm kissing you.
       Tutti frutti au rutti, *(etc.)*

4. You're the one I miss,
   I gotta tell you this.
   Oh, you're the one I miss,
   And the flavour of your kiss.
   I don't mean cherry with choc'late chips,
   I mean the same flavour as your sweet lips.
       Tutti frutti au rutti, *(etc.)*

5. Won't you be my date,
   And baby, don't be late.
   Oh, won't you be my date,
   And share my ice-cream plate.
   Without your kisses, this is all I've got,
   Just an imitation flavour of you know what.
       Tutti frutti au rutti, *(etc.)*

ROCK AROUND THE CLOCK

Words & Music by Max C. Freedman & Jimmy de Knight

With a lilt ♩ = 138

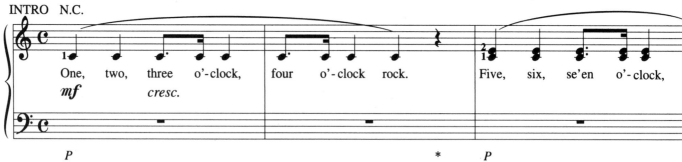

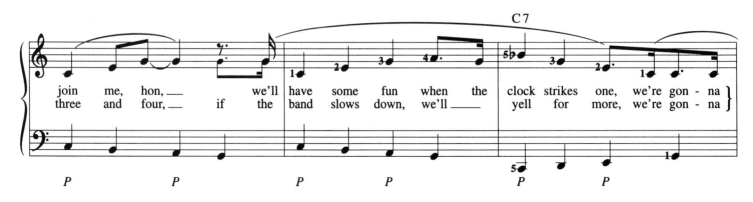

© Copyright 1953 Myers Music, USA.
© Copyright 1955 by Myers Music Limited, Exmouth House, 11 Pine Street, London EC1 for the world (excluding USA and Canada).
All Rights Reserved. International Copyright Secured.

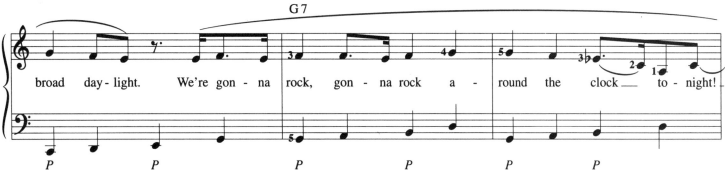

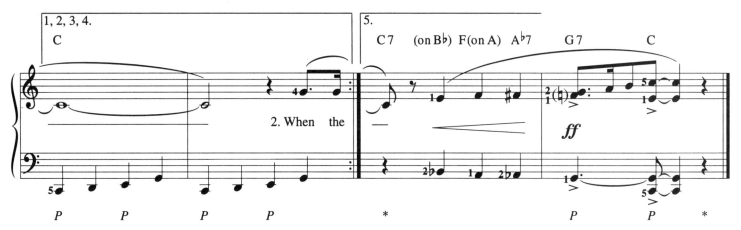

3. When the chimes ring five, and six and seven,
   We'll be rockin' up in seventh heav'n,
   We're gonna rock around the clock tonight,
   We're gonna rock, rock, rock, till broad daylight,
   We're gonna rock, gonna rock around the clock tonight!

4. When it's eight, nine, ten, eleven too,
   I'll be goin' strong, and so will you,
   We're gonna rock around the clock tonight,
   We're gonna rock, rock, rock, till broad daylight,
   We're gonna rock, gonna rock around the clock tonight!

5. When the clock strikes twelve, we'll cool off, then,
   Start a-rockin' 'round the clock again,
   We're gonna rock around the clock tonight,
   We're gonna rock, rock, rock, till broad daylight,
   We're gonna rock, gonna rock around the clock tonight!

DON'T BE CRUEL

Words & Music by Otis Blackwell & Elvis Presley

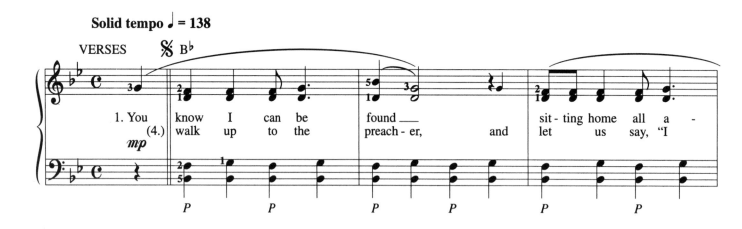

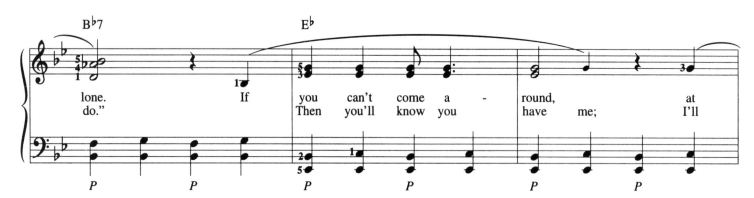

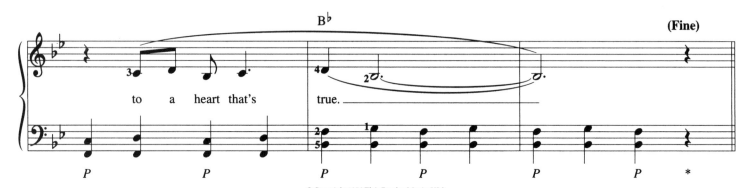

© Copyright 1956 Elvis Presley Music, USA.
Carlin Music Corporation, Iron Bridge House, 3 Bridge Approach, London NW1
for the United Kingdom of Great Britain and Northern Ireland, Eire, Israel, and the British Dominions, Colonies,
Overseas Territories and Dependencies (excluding Canada, Australia and New Zealand).
All Rights Reserved. International Copyright Secured.

GOOD GOLLY MISS MOLLY

Words & Music by Robert Blackwell & John Marascalco

© Copyright 1957 by Venice Music Incorporated, USA.
Prestige Music Limited, 1 Wyndham Yard, Wyndham Place, London W1.
All Rights Reserved. International Copyright Secured.

SEE YOU LATER ALLIGATOR

Words & Music by Robert Guidry

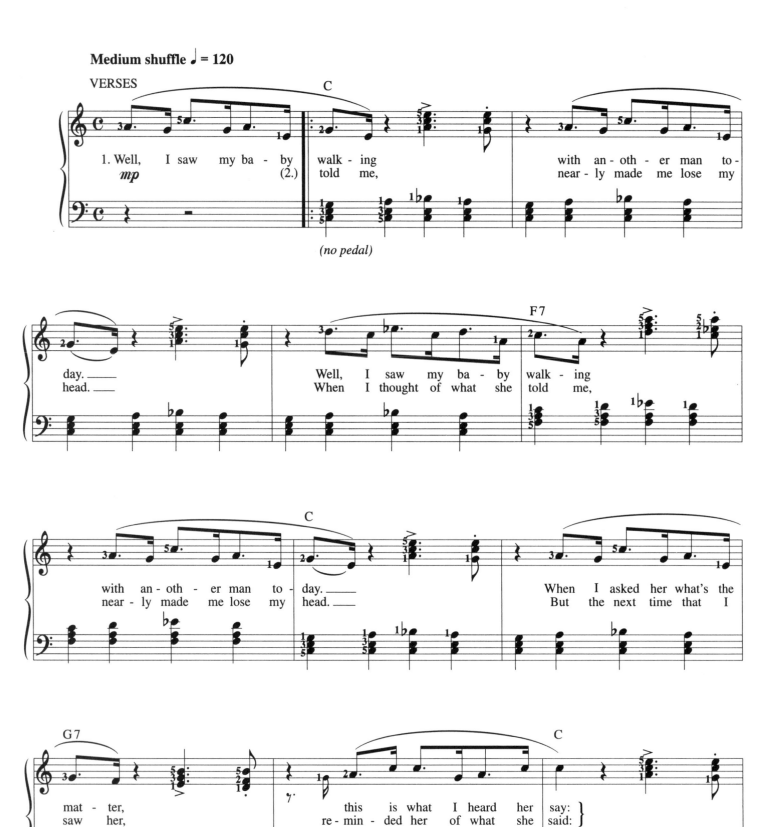

Medium shuffle ♩ = 120

VERSES

1. Well, I saw my ba-by walk-ing
(2.) told me,
with an-oth-er man to-
near-ly made me lose my

day.
head.
Well, I saw my ba-by walk-ing
When I thought of what she told me,

with an-oth-er man to-day.
near-ly made me lose my head.
When I asked her what's the
But the next time that I

mat-ter,
saw her,
this is what I heard her say:
re-min-ded her of what she said:

© Copyright 1956 Harman Music Limited. Box and Cox Publications Limited, 2/3 Fitzroy Mews, London W1.
All Rights Reserved. International Copyright Secured.

CHORUS

"See you la - ter, al - li - ga - tor, af - ter 'while, ___ cro - co -

dile. ___ See you la - ter, al - li - ga - tor, af - ter 'while ___ cro - co -

F7

dile. ___ Can't you see you're in my way, now, don't you know you cramp my

C   G7

1, 2, 3.
C

style?"   2. When I thought of what she

4.
C   D♭13   C13.9-5

style?"

3. She said, "I'm sorry, pretty daddy,
   You know my love is just for you."
   She said, "I'm sorry, pretty daddy,
   You know my love is just for you.
   Won't you say that you'll forgive me,
   And say your love for me is true?
      "See you later, alligator," *(etc.)*

4. I said, "Wait a minute, 'gator,
   I know you meant it just for play."
   I said, "Wait a minute, 'gator,
   I know you meant it just for play.
   Don't you know you really hurt me?
   And this is what I have to say:
      "See you later, alligator," *(etc.)*

THE GREAT PRETENDER

Words & Music by Buck Ram

© Copyright 1955 Panther Music Corporation, USA.
Peermusic (UK) Limited, 8-14 Verulam Street, London WC1.
All Rights Reserved. International Copyright Secured.

BE-BOP-A-LULA

Words & Music by Gene Vincent & Sheriff Tex Davis

© Copyright 1956 Lowery Music Company Incorporated.
All rights assigned to Hill & Range Songs Incorporated. Administered by Chappell & Company Incorporated, USA.
Carlin Music Corporation, Iron Bridge House, 3 Bridge Approach, London NW1
for the territory of the United Kingdom of Great Britain and Northern Ireland, Eire and the British Dominion Colonies,
Overseas Territories and Dependencies (excluding Canada, Australia and New Zealand).
All Rights Reserved. International Copyright Secured.

HEARTBREAK HOTEL

Words & Music by Mae Boren Axton, Tommy Durden & Elvis Presley

© Copyright 1956 Tree Publishing Company Incorporated,
146 W 54th Street, New York. For all countries of the world (excluding USA and Canada) Belwin Mills Music Limited.
All Rights Reserved. International Copyright Secured.

OH BOY

Words & Music by Sunny West, Bill Tilghman & Norman Petty

© Copyright 1957 MPL Communications Incorporated.
Peermusic (UK) Limited, 8-14 Verulam Street, London WC1X 8LZ.
All Rights Reserved. International Copyright Secured.

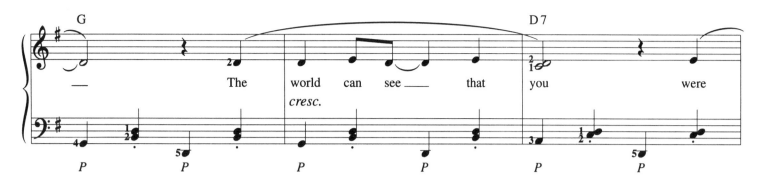

The world can see __ that you were

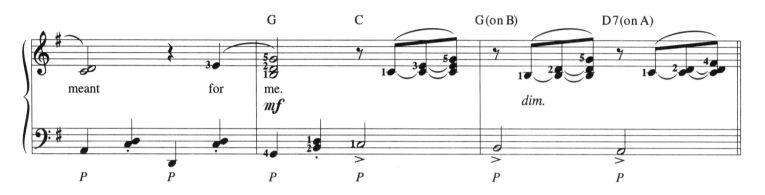

meant for me.

INTERLUDE

Dum, de dum dum, oh boy! Dum, de dum dum, oh boy!

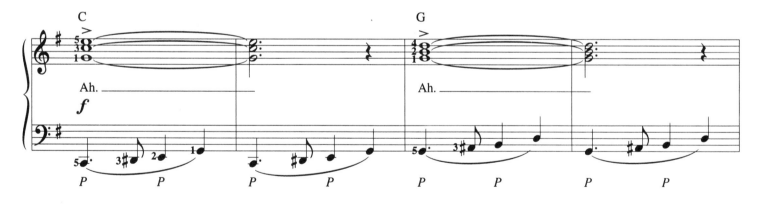

Ah. ____ Ah. ____

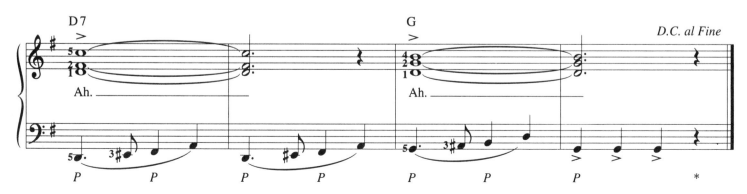

Ah. ____ Ah. ____

D.C. al Fine

25

HOUND DOG

Words & Music by Jerry Leiber & Mike Stoller

© Copyright 1956 Elvis Presley Music and Lion Publishing Company Incorporated, USA.
Edwin H. Morris & Company Limited, London.
All Rights Reserved. International Copyright Secured.

THAT'LL BE THE DAY

Words & Music by Norman Petty, Buddy Holly & Jerry Allison

© Copyright 1957 MPL Communications Incorporated.
Peermusic (UK) Limited, 8-14 Verulam Street, London WC1X 8LZ.
All Rights Reserved. International Copyright Secured.

29

JAILHOUSE ROCK

Words & Music by Jerry Leiber & Mike Stoller

© Copyright 1957 Elvis Presley Music, USA.
Carlin Music Corporation, Iron Bridge House, 3 Bridge Approach, London NW1
for the territory of United Kingdom of Great Britain & Northern Ireland, Eire, Israel and the British Dominions,
Colonies, Overseas territories and Dependencies (excluding Canada, Australia & New Zealand).
All Rights Reserved. International Copyright Secured.

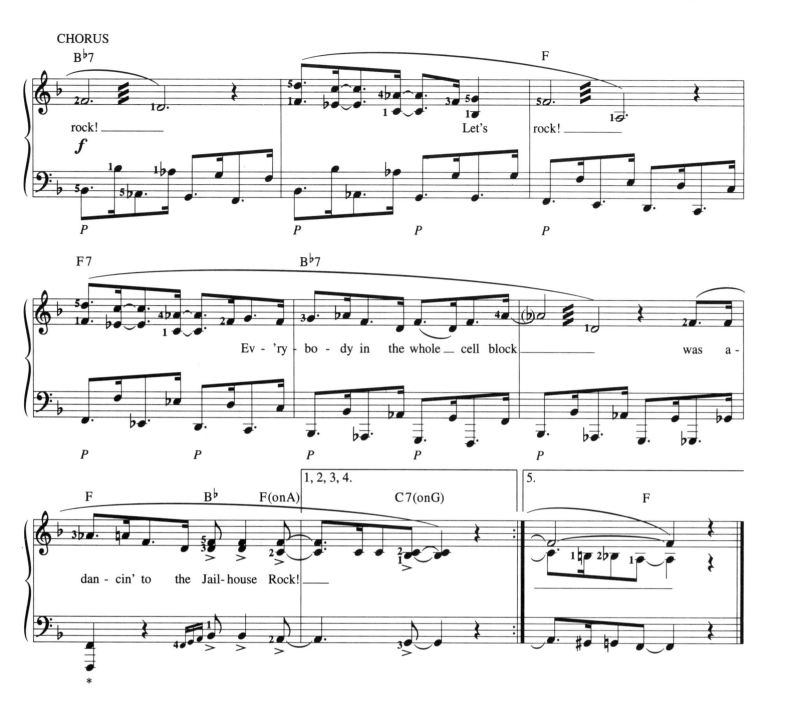

3. Number Forty-seven said to Number Three:
    "You're the cutest jailbird I ever did see,
    I sure would be delighted with your company,
    Come on and do the Jailhouse Rock with me."
        Let's rock, (etc.)

4. The sad sack was a-sittin' on a block of stone,
    Way over in the corner weeping all alone.
    The warden said: "Hey, buddy, don't you be no square,
    If you can't find a partner, use a wooden chair!"
        Let's rock, (etc.)

5. Shifty Henry said to Bugs: "For Heaven's sake,
    No one's lookin', now's our chance to make a break."
    Bugsy turned to Shifty and he said: "Nix, nix.
    I wanna stick around a while and get my kicks!"
        Let's rock, (etc.)

LONG TALL SALLY

Words & Music by Enotris Johnson, Richard Penniman & Robert Blackwell

© Copyright 1956 Venice Music Incorporated, USA.
Peermusic (UK) Limited, 8-14 Verulam Street, London WC1.
All Rights Reserved. International Copyright Secured.

JOHNNY B. GOODE

Words & Music by Chuck Berry

© Copyright 1958 Arc Music Corporation, USA.
Jewel Music Publishing Company Limited, 22 Denmark Street, London WC2.
All Rights Reserved. International Copyright Secured.

35

LAWDY MISS CLAWDY

Words & Music by Lloyd Price

© Copyright 1952 Elvis Presley Music, USA.
Carlin Music Corporation, Iron Bridge House, 3 Bridge Approach, London NW1
for the British Commonwealth (excluding Canada & Australasia) and the Republic of Ireland.
All Rights Reserved. International Copyright Secured.

AT THE HOP

Words & Music by A. Singer, J. Medora & D. White

© Copyright 1957 Arc Music Corporation, USA.
Tristan Music Limited, 22 Denmark Street, London WC2.
All Rights Reserved. International Copyright Secured.

CHORUS

Let's go to the hop, ___ (oh ba - by,)

let's go to the hop, ___ (oh ba - by,) let's go to the hop, ___

___ (oh ba - by,) let's go to the hop, ___ (oh ba - by,)

come on, let's go to the hop. ___

___ 2. Oh, you can let's go to the hop.

LUCILLE

Words & Music by Albert Collins & Richard Penniman

Medium boogie ♩ = 126

© Copyright 1957 ATV Music.
All Rights Reserved. International Copyright Secured.

BLUE SUEDE SHOES

Words & Music by Carl Lee Perkins

Firmly ♩ = 132

© Copyright 1956 by Hi-Lo Music all rights assigned to Hill & Range Songs Incorporated,
administered by Unichappell Music Incorporated, New York, USA.
Carlin Music Corporation, Iron Bridge House, 3 Bridge Approach, London NW1
for the territory of United Kingdom of Great Britain & Northern Ireland, Israel & the British Dominions, Colonies,
Overseas Territories & Dependencies (excluding Canada, Australia & New Zealand) (also excluding South Africa).
All Rights Reserved. International Copyright Secured.

GREAT BALLS OF FIRE

Words & Music by Jack Hammer & Otis Blackwell

© Copyright 1957 B.R.S. Music Corporation, all rights assigned to Chappell & Company Incorporated, USA.
Carlin Music Corporation, Iron Bridge House, 3 Bridge Approach, London NW1 for the United Kingdom, British Commonwealth
(Excluding Canada & Australasia) and the Republic of Ireland and Israel.
All Rights Reserved. International Copyright Secured.

PEGGY SUE

Words & Music by Jerry Allison, Norman Petty & Buddy Holly

© Copyright 1957 MPL Communications Incorporated.
Peermusic (UK) Limited, 8-14 Verulam Street, London WC1.
All Rights Reserved. International Copyright Secured.

11/03 (49434)